the source

arrangements for worship groups

book 1

E♭ instruments

arranged by Chris Mitchell

Kevin Mayhew

We hope you enjoy the music in this book.
Further copies of this and the other books in the series are available
from your local music shop or Christian bookshop.

In case of difficulty, please contact the publisher direct:

The Sales Department
KEVIN MAYHEW LTD
Rattlesden
Bury St Edmunds
Suffolk IP30 0SZ

Phone 01449 737978
Fax 01449 737834

Please ask for our complete catalogue of outstanding Church Music.

First published in Great Britain in 1998 by Kevin Mayhew Ltd.

ISBN 1 84003 249 9
ISMN M 57004 439 9
Catalogue No: 1470313

0 1 2 3 4 5 6 7 8 9

Cover designed by Jaquetta Sergeant

Music arrangements by Chris Mitchell
Music Editor: Alistair McPherson
Music setting by Lynwen Davies and Chris Mitchell

Printed and bound in Great Britain

Contents

This index gives the first line of each hymn. If a hymn is known by an alternative title, this is also given, but indented and in italics.

CHRIS MITCHELL is a well-established arranger, composer, musical director and session musician who has worked with Graham Kendrick, David Peacock, Gloria Gaynor and the BBC. He and his wife, Linda, are experienced worship leaders and are involved in providing seminars and workshops for Christians in the arts.

1 Abba, Father, let me be

Dave Bilbrough

2 Abide with me

William Henry Monk

5 verses

3 Above the clash of creeds
(No other way)

Graham Kendrick

3 verses

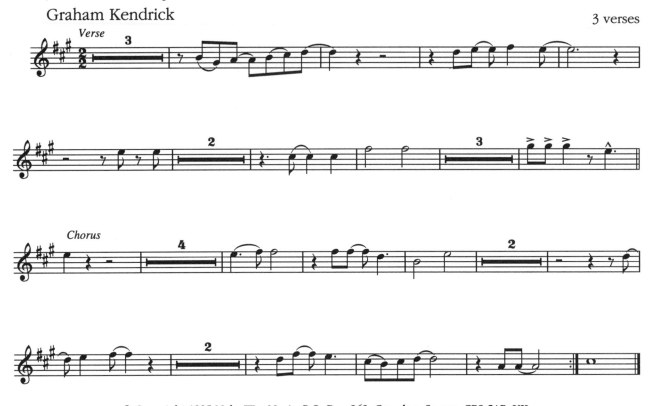

4 Alleluia, alleluia, give thanks to the risen Lord

Donald Fishel

5 verses

5 All hail King Jesus!

Dave Moody

Worshipfully with strength

6 All hail the Lamb

Dave Bilbrough

With awe

7 All hail the power of Jesus' name (Tune 1)

William Shrubsole

6 verses

7a All hail the power of Jesus' name (Tune 2)

James Ellor

6 verses

8 All heaven declares

Noel and Tricia Richards

2 verses

9 All heaven waits

Graham Kendrick

5 verses

10 All honour, all glory

Chris Falson

11 All I once held dear
(Knowing you)

Graham Kendrick

Smoothly

3 verses

12 All over the world

Terry Butler

2 verses

13 All people that on earth do dwell

From the *Genevan Psalter*

5 verses

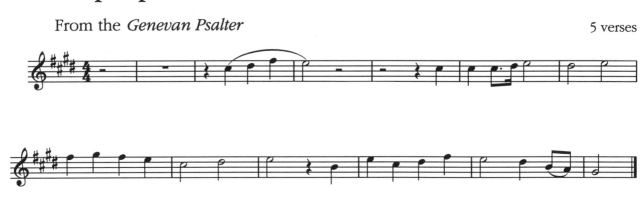

14 All things bright and beautiful (Tune 1)

Traditional English melody

4 verses

14a All things bright and beautiful (Tune 2)

William Henry Monk

4 verses

15 All to Jesus I surrender
(I surrender all)

W.S. Weedon

5 verses

Verse

Chorus

16 Almighty God, we bring you praise

Austin Martin

Worshipfully

17 Almighty God, my Redeemer
(All things are possible)

Darlene Zschech

18 Amazing grace

American folk melody

6 verses

19 Among the gods
(You alone are God)

Carol Owen

20 An army of ordinary people

Dave Bilbrough

2 verses

With feeling

21 And can it be

Thomas Campbell

5 verses

22 And he shall reign

Graham Kendrick

3 verses

23 A new commandment

Unknown

24 Anointing, fall on me

Donn Charles Thomas

25 Ascribe greatness

Peter West, Mary Lou Locke and Mary Kirkbride

26 As I come into your presence
(Awesome in this place)

Dave Billington

27 As the deer pants

Martin J. Nystrom

Flowing

28 As the deer pants
(Your waves of love)

Richard Lewis

Rhythmically

29 As we are gathered

John Daniels

30 As we lift up your name
(Revival fire, fall)

Paul Baloche

2 verses

31 As we seek your face

Dave Bilbrough

3 verses

32 At the foot of the cross

Derek Bond

33 At the name of Jesus

Michael Brierley

7 verses

34 At this time of giving
(The giving song)

Graham Kendrick

3 verses

Accelerating with each verse

35 At your feet we fall

David Fellingham

3 verses

With steady strength

36 Away in a manger

William James Kirkpatrick

3 verses

37 Beauty for brokenness
(God of the poor)

Graham Kendrick

5 verses

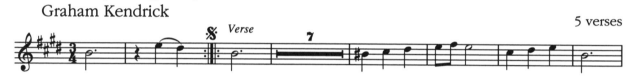

38 Be bold, be strong

Morris Chapman

39 Because of your love

Russell Fragar

40 Before the world began
(So you would come)

Russell Fragar

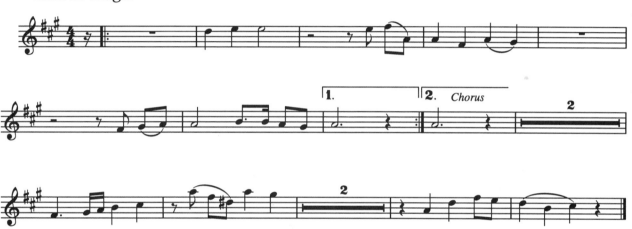

41 Be free

Dave Bilbrough

2 verses

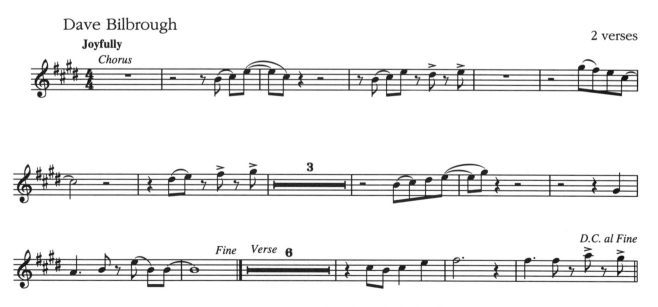

42 Be glorified

Billy Funk

2 verses

43 Behold his love

Geoff Baker

44 Behold the Lord

Noel Richards and Gerald Coates

3 verses

45 Beneath the cross of Jesus

Frederick C. Maker

5 verses

46 Be patient, be ready

(White horse)

Graham Kendrick

47 Be still, for the presence of the Lord

David J. Evans

3 verses

48 Be still and know

Unknown

3 verses

49 Be still, my soul

Jean Sibelius

3 verses

© Copyright Breitkopf and Härtel, Walkmühlstrasse 52, D-65195 Wiesbaden, Germany.
Used by permission.

50 Be thou my vision

Traditional Irish melody

5 verses

51 Bind us together

Bob Gillman

Easy waltz feel

3 verses

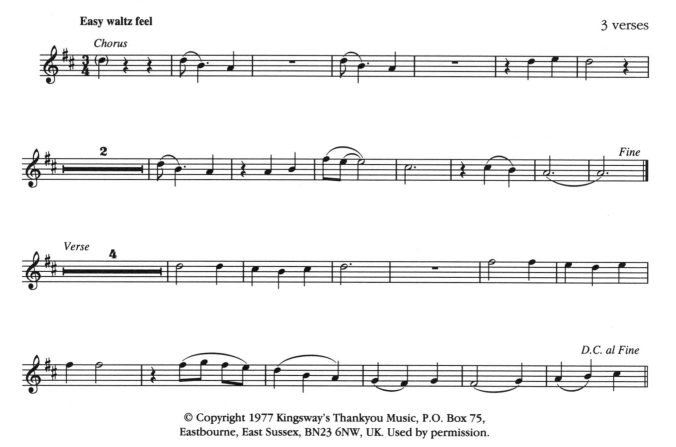

52 Blessed assurance, Jesus is mine

Phoebe Palmer Knapp

3 verses

53 Blessed be the name of the Lord

Kevin Prosch and Danny Daniels

2 verses

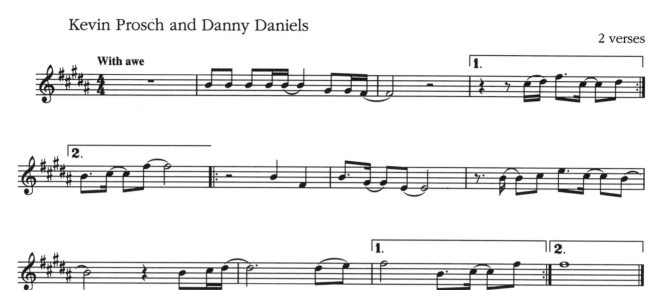

54 Blessing and honour
(Ancient of Days)

Gary Sadler and Jamie Harvill

With an 'island' feel

55 Blessing, honour, glory to the Lamb
(Glory to the Lamb)

Geoff Bullock and Dave Reidy

56 Bless the Lord, my soul

Jacques Berthier

57 Breathe on me, Breath of God (Tune 1)

Charles Lockhart

4 verses

57a Breathe on me, Breath of God (Tune 2)

Robert Jackson

4 verses

58 Broken for me

Janet Lunt

4 verses

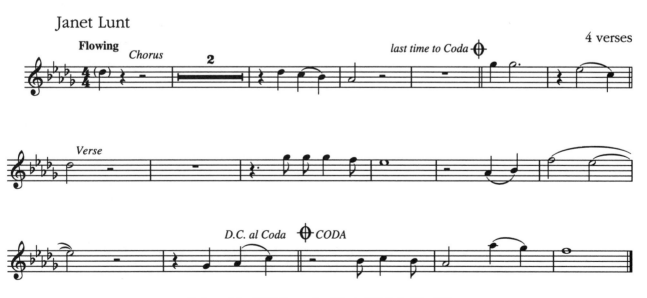

59 By his grace

Steven Fry

60 By your side

Noel and Tricia Richards

61 Called to a battle
(Thunder in the skies)

Noel and Tricia Richards

2 verses

62 Can a nation be changed?

Matt Redman

2 verses

63 Can I ascend
(I'm coming up the mountain)

Matt Redman

Rhythmically

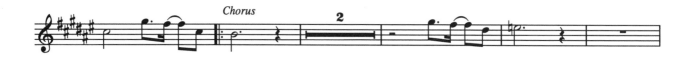

64 Can we walk upon the water

Matt Redman

2 verses

65 Can you see what we have made
(Song for Christingle)

Graham Kendrick

5 verses

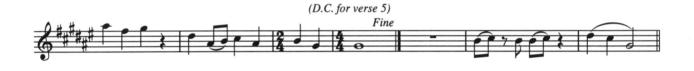

66 Celebrate, celebrate

(Seven reasons to celebrate)

Graham Kendrick

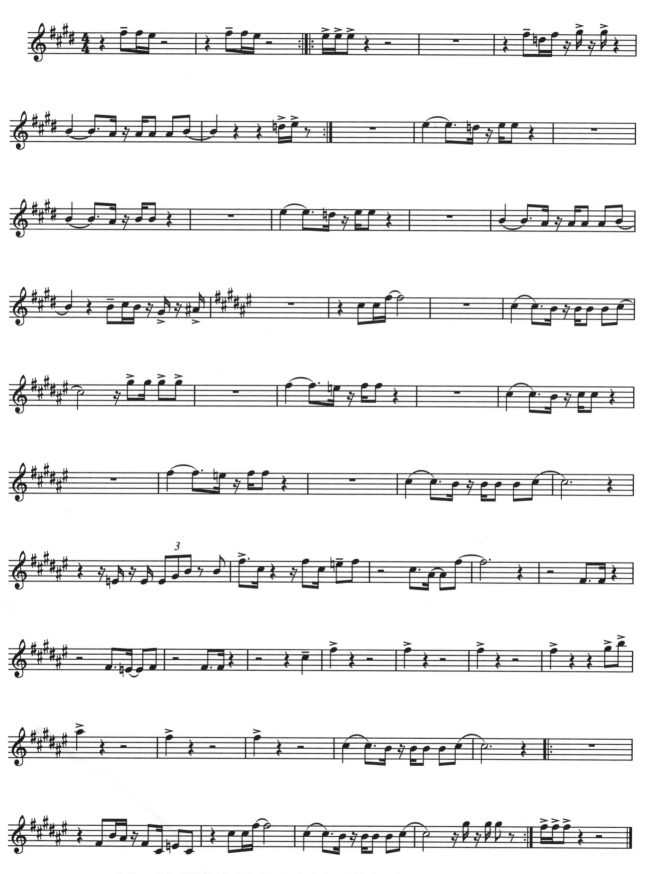

67 Celebrate Jesus

Gary Oliver

68 Change my heart, O God

Eddie Espinosa

69 Colours of day
(Light up the fire)

Sue McClellan, John Paculabo and Keith Ryecroft

3 verses

Flowing

70 Come and see
(We worship at your feet)

Graham Kendrick

3 verses

Worshipfully

71 Come down, O Love divine

Ralph Vaughan Williams

4 verses

72 Come, let us return

Graham Kendrick

73 Come, let us worship Jesus
(King of the nations)

Graham Kendrick

5 verses

74 Come on, all us singers, sing
(Singers' song)

2 verses

Martin Smith

75 Come on and celebrate
(Celebrate)
Patricia Morgan and Dave Bankhead

76 Come, Spirit, come

Elizabeth Bourbourze

3 verses

77 Crown him with many crowns

George Job Elvey

5 verses

78 Day of favour

David Fellingham

2 verses

79 Dear Lord and Father of mankind

Charles Hubert Hastings Parry

5 verses

80 Did you feel the mountains tremble?

Martin Smith

3 verses

81 Don't let my love grow cold
(Light the fire again)

Brian Doerksen

82 Do something new, Lord

Chris Bowater

3 verses

83 Down the mountain the river flows
(The river is here)

Andy Park

3 verses

With joy

Verse

84 Draw me closer

Stuart Devane and Glenn Gore

Flowing

85 Earth lies spellbound

Graham Kendrick

3 verses

86 Every nation, power and tongue

Russell Fragar

87 Exalt the Lord

Mike and Claire McIntosh

88 Faithful God

Chris Bowater

Worshipfully and unhurried

89 Faithful One

Brian Doerksen

90 Far and near
(Say it loud)

Graham Kendrick

3 verses

91 Father God, I wonder
(I will sing your praises)

Ian Smale

92 Father God, we worship you

Graham Kendrick

3 verses

Worshipfully

93 Father, hear our prayer

Andy Piercy

Meditatively

94 Father, here I am
(Let forgiveness flow)
Danny Daniels

With feeling

95 Father, I come to you
(Unending love)
John Barnett

3 verses

Gently

Verse

Chorus

to verses   *last time*

96 Father in heaven, how we love you
(Blessed be the Lord God Almighty)
Bob Fitts

97 Father, I place into your hands
Jenny Hewer

4 verses

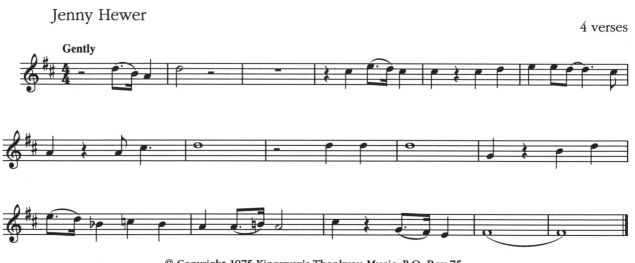

98 Father, I want you to hold me
Brian Doerksen

2 verses

99 Father of creation
(Let your glory fall)

David Ruis

2 verses

With strength

100 Father of life, draw me closer
(Let the peace of God reign)

Darlene Zschech